but

Cub Can

by Liza Charlesworth

ISBN: 978-1-338-78272-1
Illustrated by Chester Bentley

Published by Scholastic Inc., 557 Broadway, New York, NY 10012

10 9 8 7 6 5 4 3 2 1 68 21 22 23 24 25 26 27/0

Printed in Jiaxing, China. First printing, June 2021.

SCHOLASTIC

Bee can fly.
But Cub cannot fly.

Butterfly can fly.
But Cub cannot fly.

Bird can fly.
But Cub cannot fly.

Duck can fly.
But Cub cannot fly.

Owl can fly.
But Cub cannot fly.

Bat can fly.
But Cub cannot fly.

Kite can fly.
Cub can fly, too!